An Africentric Primer for Young Readers

THE ADVENTURES OF KOJO AND AMA

by

Nkechi Taifa

Illustrations by Afia Nson Bonsu

DEDICATION

Dedicated to my niece Tina Lanae Drake, who departed this earthly plane far too soon, secreting within herself many exciting unwritten story threads, and to my daughter Mariama Taifa-Seitu for being the inspiration throughout my life.

Thanks to all who helped birth the original edition of this book, and thanks to all who help keep this message relevant, bringing the word to new audiences.

TABLE OF CONTENTS

INTRODUCTION

Kojo and Ama are names from Ghana, West Africa. Kojo means a boy born on Monday. It sounds like "KOH-jo." Ama means a girl born on Saturday. It sounds like "AH-mah." Kojo and Ama live in a city in the United States with Mama, Daddy, and Sheba the Cat. Take a journey with Kojo and Ama and share their adventures in these seven exciting stories!

SHEBA THE CAT

Kojo and Ama have a cat. Her name is Sheba the Cat. Sheba brings good luck. She helps Kojo and Ama when they need help. Sheba the Cat is a good pet.

One day, Ama fell in a hole and hurt her leg.

"Ouch! I'm hurt!" Ama cried. "Kojo, please come and help me!"

Kojo was at home. He did not hear Ama. Kojo didn't know his sister was hurt.

Sheba the Cat heard Ama cry for help. She ran to help Ama.

"Sheba the Cat, I'm glad you came!" said Ama. "I need help. I will tie a note to your tail. Go home and get Kojo. The note will tell him I'm hurt."

Sheba the Cat ran and ran. She had a job to do. She had to take the note to Kojo.

'Meow-Meow, I smell a mouse,' said Sheba the Cat. *'I will not stop to catch it. Ama is hurt.'*

Sheba the Cat ran and ran. *'Meow-Meow, I see a coil of rope,'* she said. *'I will not stop to play with it. I have a job to do.'*

Sheba ran on. She stopped when she saw Jack the Cat. *'Meow-Meow,'* said Jack. *'I found some fish. Stay and eat it with me, Sheba.'*

'No, Jack,' said Sheba the Cat. *'I have a job to do. Ama needs help. I have a note for Kojo. I must go now.'*

Sheba the Cat saw a man with a scar on his arm. The man said, "Scat you bad cat."

Sheba ran and ran. She ran to find Kojo.

Sheba the Cat saw a man with a red, black, and green cap.

The man smiled at Sheba.

Sheba the Cat purred, but ran on. *'Meow-Meow, I must not let Ama down,'* said Sheba the Cat. *'She is a good girl.'*

Sheba the Cat ran home. She ran up to Kojo and rubbed his leg. *'Meow-Meow!'* said Sheba the Cat.

"I see a note on your tail," said Kojo. "What is it?"

Kojo read the note. The note said:

> *Dear Kojo,*
> *   Please help me. I fell in the big hole and hurt*
> *my leg. Come and help me. Please come fast.*
> *   Your sister,*
> *   Ama*

Kojo gave Sheba the Cat a pat on her back and a rub on her fur. "You're a good cat," he said.

'Purr, Purr,' said Sheba the Cat.

Kojo ran to help Ama. Sheba the Cat ran with Kojo. They ran past the man with the red, black, and green cap. He smiled at them. They ran past the man with the scar on his arm. He frowned at them. They ran past Jack the Cat as he ate his fish.

Jack the Cat purred at them. They ran past the mouse. The mouse ran away fast. They ran past the coil of rope. Sheba the Cat stopped by the coil of rope.

"Don't stop now," said Kojo. "Ama needs our help!" Sheba the Cat did not budge. She sat down by the rope. "Oh, yes," said Kojo. "Sheba, you're a smart cat! The rope
can help Ama."

Kojo ran with the rope to the big hole. Sheba the Cat went with him. Kojo tied the rope to a tree and put part of the rope down the hole.

"Put the rope on your waist," Kojo said to Ama. "I'll pull you out of the hole."

"Kojo, I'm glad you came!" said Ama.

Kojo held the rope firm. The rope helped Kojo pull Ama out of the hole.

"Kojo, thank you," said Ama. "I'm safe now."

"Don't thank me," said Kojo. "Thank Sheba the Cat. She's a smart pet. Sheba the Cat brings us lots of luck."

DANGER IN THE PARK
AFTER DARK

Kojo and Ama went to the park. "Let's play!" said Kojo. "I'll sit on the swing," said Ama.

"I'll play on the slide," said Kojo.

Kojo and Ama played and played. Soon it was dusk. "Look!" said Ama. "The moon is full. We stayed at the park too late. It's time to go home."

"Wait!" said Kojo. "I want to play on the slide one more time. Then we'll go home."

Ama sat on the swing to wait. Kojo did not slide just one last time. Kojo played and played.

"Look, Kojo, look!" said Ama. "I see a big star. If you look at the big star and make a wish, the wish will come true."

"I wish I didn't have to go home," said Kojo.

Soon a strange man came to the park. He had a scar on his arm and a big stick in his hand.

"Look!" said Ama. "That man has a big stick!"

"Let's run!" said Kojo. "I'm ready to go home now. The park is not a good place to be when it's dark!"

Ama ran fast.

The strange man said, "Stop!"

Ama ran and ran. She did not stop. Kojo ran fast.

The strange man said, "Stop!"

Kojo ran and fell down. "Oh, no!" said Kojo. "My shoe made me trip. I didn't tie it."

"Don't get up!" the stranger said to Kojo. "Don't run. I want you to hold my little bag."

"I don't want to hold your bag," said Kojo. "I want to go home!"

"If you don't hold my bag, I'll hit you with my stick!" the stranger said.

Kojo held the little bag.

"Now get up!" the stranger said. "Get up and go sit on the swing. A friend in a big car will drive to the park. He'll have on a big white hat and a blue tie. Give the bag to him. Here's some cash."

"I don't want your money!" Kojo said. "I don't want to hold your bag and I don't like your stick. I want to go home!"

The stranger hid by a tree. He still had the big stick. Kojo sat on the swing. He didn't want to get hit with the stick.

Just then the man with the big white hat and blue tie drove up to the park. He looked mean. "Give the bag to me!" he said.

Kojo gave the man the bag. "Now get in the car!" he said to Kojo.

Kojo looked up at the moon. He looked at the big star. Kojo made a big wish.

Just then Sheba the Cat sprang from a tree with a loud hiss. "Oh, no!" the mean man said as he leaped back. "I see a cat. I don't want that cat to cross my path!" Sheba the Cat hissed again, louder this time.

The two strangers ran. The little bag fell from the hand of the mean man. They ran and drove off in the big car.

"Sheba, you saved my life!" said Kojo. "You're a great cat!"

Just then Kojo saw a man with a red, black, and green cap. "Are you safe?" the man asked. "I saw a little girl run. She said her brother was in danger."

"I'm fine now," Kojo said. "Ama was smart. She ran for help. She didn't trip."

"Tell me what happened," the man with the red, black, and green cap said.

"A man with a big stick made me take his bag. He made me give the bag to the mean man with the big white hat and blue tie."

The man with the red, black, and green cap got mad. "Then I made a wish for help," said Kojo. "Sheba the Cat

came to help. She scared the two men! They ran off."

Sheba the Cat gave a scratch by the tree. "Look!" the man with the red, black, and green cap said. "Is that the bag by the tree?" He went to the tree and picked up the bag.

Drugs!" he said with a frown as he opened the bag. "Drugs are bad. Don't ever take drugs!" he said. "Don't ever sell drugs. Drugs can harm your body and mind."

"I won't ever take drugs!" said Kojo. "I want to keep my mind clear and my body strong."

Just then Daddy came to the park. "Kojo, are you safe?" Daddy asked. Daddy gave Kojo a big hug. He held him for a long time.

Daddy looked at the man with the red, black, and green cap. "Who are you?" Daddy asked.

"My name is Brother Shaka," the man with the red, black, and green cap said to Daddy.

"Nice to meet you," said Daddy.

"Your son is safe." Brother Shaka said. "The cat gave the drug dealers a big scare. They drove off."

"You are very brave," Daddy said to Kojo. "But remember, do not stay at the park after dark!"

"Thanks for your help," Daddy said to Brother Shaka. "Don't thank me," Brother Shaka said. "Thank the cat. She gave good luck."

Daddy gave Sheba the Cat a pat on her back and a rub on her fur. Sheba the Cat gave Daddy a purr.

THE MAN WITH THE RED, BLACK, AND GREEN CAP

Brother Shaka became good friends with Mama and Daddy. He often took Kojo and Ama many places.

"I'm going to the library to return a book," Brother Shaka said to Mama one day. "Can I take Kojo and Ama with me?"

"Yes," Mama smiled. "My children love books! Let me get their library cards."

The library was too far to walk, so Kojo, Ama, and Brother Shaka rode the bus.

"Brother Shaka, why do you wear that red, black, and green cap?" Kojo asked as they sat down.

"The red, black, and green colors in my cap make me feel proud," he said.

"How do they make you feel proud?" asked Ama.

"The red, black, and green stands for the flag of African people all over. The red stands for the blood that has been shed. The black stands for African people wherever they may be in the world. The green stands for land. The red, black, and green gives me hope."

"What if you lose your red, black, and green cap?" asked Kojo.

Brother Shaka smiled. "I may lose my cap, but I will never lose my pride," he said. "I may lose my cap, but I will never lose my hope."

"The colors red, black, and green are on your book," said Ama. "Does the book give you pride?"

"Yes," Brother Shaka said. "This book tells many stories which make me feel proud."

"What are the stories about?" asked Ama.

"The stories in my book are about African American people and the many great deeds they did."

"Tell us about what they did!" said Kojo.

Brother Shaka looked up. "Why did the bus stop?" he asked Kojo and Ama.

"The bus stopped for the red light," Ama said.

Brother Shaka smiled. He opened his big book. "Did you know that the first stop light was made by an African American? His name was Garrett Morgan. He made the stop light so it would be safe to cross the street. Do not forget about him."

"Tell us more from your book!" Kojo and Ama said. "What time is it?" Brother Shaka asked.

"I don't know," said Kojo.

"There isn't a clock on the bus," said Ama. "Benjamin Banneker made the first clock in America," Brother Shaka said.

"He was born a free man during the time of slavery. He used a telescope to study the stars. He wrote an almanac which is a book with many facts. He also made the plans for the streets of Washington, D.C. Benjamin Banneker was a very wise man."

"Tell us more," said Kojo and Ama as the bus rolled along. "We like your book!"

Although Brother Shaka turned the page, he seemed to know the stories by heart. "Lewis Latimer made the light bulbs shine bright. He put a strong wire in the bulb so the light would not fade as fast. He was very skilled. Lewis Latimer was a smart man."

"I want to be a doctor when I grow up," said Ama. "Does your book tell about any African American doctors?"

"Daniel Hale Williams was a great doctor!" Brother Shaka said.

"A man had a bad heart. Dr. Williams opened the man's chest and made his heart well."

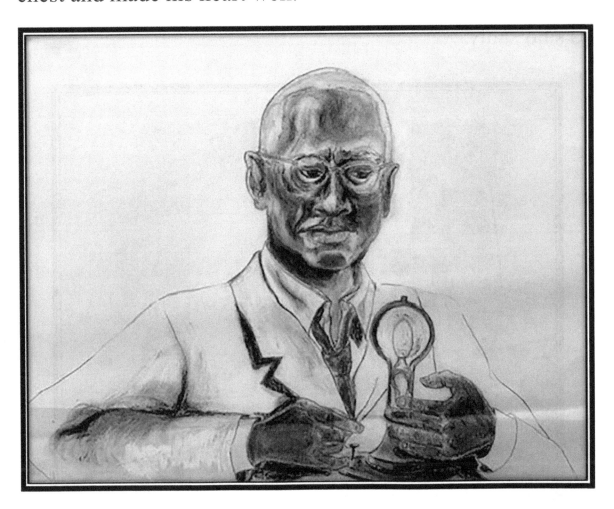

"This was called open heart surgery. Daniel Hale Williams was the first to do this."

"Tell us more!" Ama said with pride.

"Charles Drew was a doctor. He made a way to keep blood so it wouldn't spoil. He stored the blood in blood banks which kept it fresh. When people who were hurt needed blood, doctors went to the blood banks. Thousands of lives were saved because of Charles Drew."

"That's great!" said Kojo.

"Yes, that was great, but even though this country had blood banks, some people still died from the loss of blood," Brother Shaka said sadly.

"I don't understand," said Kojo.

Brother Shaka took off his red, black, and green cap.

He spoke in a low tone. "One night when I was a little boy, my grandfather's car was hit. He was hurt and lost a lot of blood. My grandfather could not get blood from a blood bank because the hospital that was near to his car would not let Black people come in for help. Grandfather died from the loss of blood."

"That's terrible!" said Kojo.

"Yes, that's a real shame," said Ama.

"There were once many laws in America that were not fair to African Americans," Brother Shaka said.

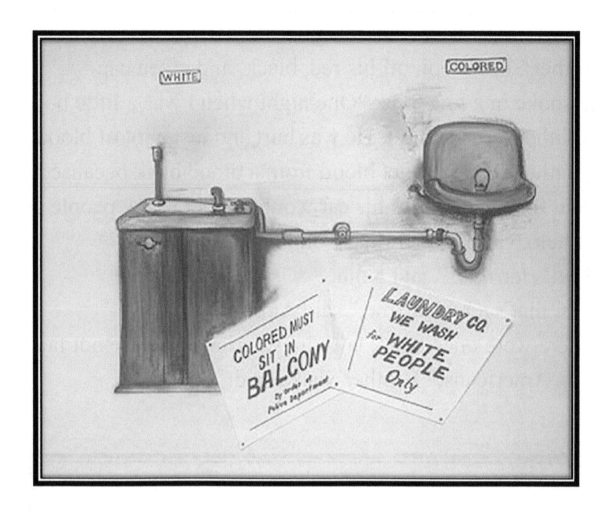

"There were laws that said Black people could not enter through the front doors of stores. There were laws that said Black people could not vote. There were laws that said Black people could not go in some parks or go to some schools.

"Did people try to change those unfair laws?" asked Ama. "Yes," Brother Shaka said as he put his red, black, and green cap back on his head. "There are many tales about what brave people did to try and change the unfair laws. I will just tell you one tale. We're on a bus, so I'll tell you about Rosa Parks."

"A lady got off from her job late one day. She had to wait for the bus. Her name was Rosa Parks. The law said that African Americans had to sit in the back of the bus. Rosa Parks didn't see a seat in the back of the bus, so she sat in a seat near the front."

"The bus driver got up and came to Rosa Parks. 'Get up!' he said."

"Rosa Parks did not stand up. 'I paid for my seat on this bus,' she said. 'The law is not fair.'"

"'If you don't get up, I'll put you in jail!' the bus driver said."

"Did Rosa Parks get out of her seat?" asked Ama.

"No, she didn't," Brother Shaka said, "so she was put in jail."

"That's terrible!" said Kojo. "What happened next?"

"The people had a big meeting where they asked Rev. Martin Luther King to help them try to change the law. With his leadership, they made a plan to stop riding the buses. This was called a bus boycott. It lasted a whole year. The boycott made the bus company lose a lot of money. Then the law was changed to let all people sit anywhere on the bus."

"I'm glad Rosa Parks was brave," said Ama. "The law was not fair."

"Look, there's the library!" Brother Shaka said. "The bus is at our stop."

"I want to get a book like yours," Kojo said.

"Yes, I like the stories your book tells about great people," said Ama. "They make me feel proud."

SMOKE AND FLAMES

Uncle Bob is visiting Kojo and Ama. Mama and Daddy like Uncle Bob to visit, but they don't like some of the things he likes to do.

"Uncle Bob, why do you smoke?" Ama asked. "Mama says it's bad for you."

"Yes, the smoke is bad for your lungs," said Kojo.

"I like to smoke," Uncle Bob said. "I like to drink. I like to watch T.V. all of the time. I know it's bad to smoke, but it's hard for me to stop."

"Kojo and Ama, it's time to go to bed," said Mama. "Take your bath and brush your teeth."

"I want to stay up late and watch T.V.," said Kojo.

"I want to stay up late and play cards with Uncle Bob," said Ama.

"Kojo and Ama, you will go to bed now!" Mama said.

Kojo and Ama did as they were told. They gave Mama and Daddy a kiss and went upstairs.

Sheba the Cat gave Mama and Daddy a purr.

Uncle Bob sat in the chair. He smoked and drank. He watched T.V. His eyes closed.

Mama knew Uncle Bob was going to fall asleep.

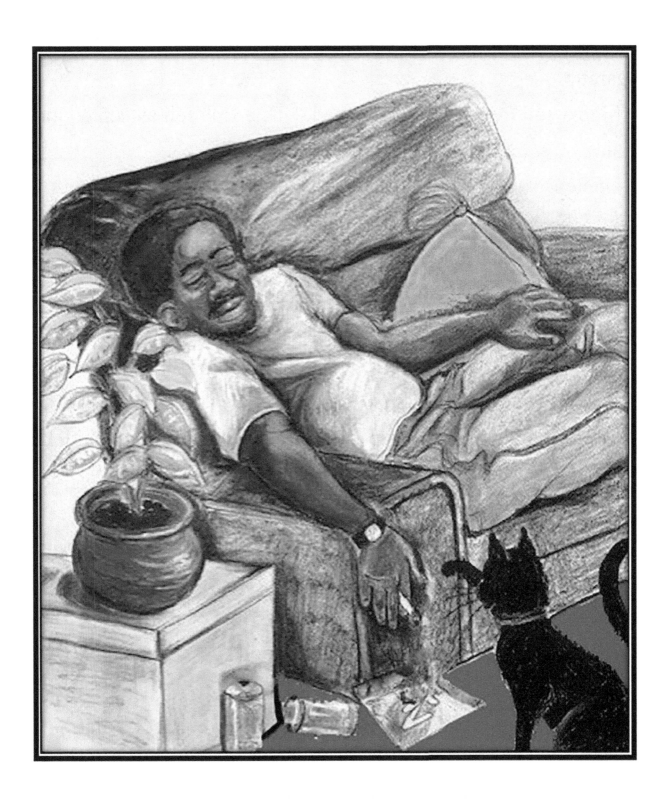

"Uncle Bob, go up to bed," Mama said. "Don't sleep on the chair!"

"I'll go up to bed soon," Uncle Bob said as he puffed on his cigarette.

Mama and Daddy went up to bed. Uncle Bob fell asleep on the chair.

Uncle Bob began to snore. The cigarette fell out of his mouth. It fell on the rug close to the magazine. The magazine pages began to burn. They burned and burned.

Sheba the Cat woke up with a start. Her tail went up.

Her nose went up. The fur on her back rose up.

'Meow-Meow,' said Sheba the Cat. '*I smell smoke! The smoke is bad. I will rub Uncle Bob's leg,*' Sheba said.

Uncle Bob did not wake up. '*I will lick his face,*' Sheba said. Uncle Bob did not wake up. '*I will scratch his nose,*' Sheba said.

"Ouch!" said Uncle Bob, but he still did not wake up.

'*The smell of the smoke is strong,*' said Sheba the Cat. '*The rug is on fire. I will wake Mama and Daddy up,*' she said.

'Meow-Meow,' said Sheba the Cat. Daddy woke up. 'Meow-Meow,' said Sheba the Cat. Mama woke up. "I smell smoke!" said Daddy. "It's hot in here."

"I see flames!" said Mama. "I did not hear the smoke alarm. Wake up, Kojo!"

"Quick, get up Ama!" Daddy said. "We must leave our home fast. Close the door! We must keep the smoke out. It's bad for the lungs to smell the smoke from the flames."

"I'll stuff rags to seal the crack in the door," Mama said.

Then the smoke won't seep in. Both the smoke and flames can harm us!"

"Where is Uncle Bob!?" asked Ama.

"Uncle Bob is on the chair," said Mama. "He's close to the front door. He should be safe."

"Where is Sheba the Cat!?" Kojo yelled.

"Don't yell," Daddy said to Kojo. "Don't scream. Stay calm."

"Sheba the Cat woke us up," said Mama. "She's a smart cat. She won't get hurt."

"We can leave by the window," said Daddy. "We will lean on the big ledge. We'll be safe."

Sheba the Cat went back downstairs. '*I must wake up Uncle Bob,*' she said. '*He must have had too much beer to drink. I will jump on his chair. I will bite his nose.*' Sheba the Cat bit Uncle Bob's nose.

"Ouch!" said Uncle Bob. Uncle Bob woke up. "Get away, bad cat!" he shouted. Then Uncle Bob saw the flames. "Oh, no!" he yelled. "I can't get out! The flames are too close to the door. Oh, no!" he yelled. "The smoke is in my nose. It's hard for me to breathe. I can hear the fire truck. I don't know if they can save us in time," he said to Sheba the Cat.

The fire fighter put a hose in the house. The water came out hard and fast. The fire was put out. Uncle Bob and Sheba the Cat were safe.

The fire fighter put a ladder to the side of the house. "Climb down," he said. Ama climbed down the ladder. Kojo climbed down the ladder. Mama climbed down the ladder.

Daddy climbed down the ladder. The family was now safe. "I feel bad," Uncle Bob said to Kojo and Ama. "I won't

smoke anymore. I don't want to harm our family. I don't want to harm our lungs."

"You must check your smoke alarm to make sure it works," the fire fighter said to Mama and Daddy.

"You're lucky you woke up!"

Uncle Bob gave Sheba the Cat a pat on her back and a rub on her fur. "You saved my life!" he said. "You're a good cat. You're a smart cat. You bring good luck!"

FUN IN THE SUN

"Ama and I are going on a trip," Kojo said to Brother Shaka with a smile. "We're going with Mama and Daddy on a big plane to Jamaica. It'll be a long ride."

"That's great!" Brother Shaka said. "Jamaica is a place where there's lots of sunshine. You'll have fun there!"

"Will you feed Sheba the Cat while we're gone?" asked Ama.

"Yes, I will," said Brother Shaka. "Sheba the Cat is a good pet. I'll take care of her."

The big plane took the family to Jamaica. It was a long ride.

Kojo and Ama looked out their hotel window the next

"Look at the sun!" said Ama. "See it coming up in the east?"

"Look at the trees," said Kojo. "The leaves are very big in Jamaica!"

"Daddy, can we go to the beach?" the children asked.

"That sounds like fun," said Daddy. "Mama and I will sit on the sand and watch you play."

The family went down to the beach.

"Look!" said Kojo. "I see a boy. Let's go meet him."

"Hi, I'm Kojo," he said to the boy. "This is Ama."

"Hey mon," the boy said with a smile. "My name is Rafiki."

"Where do you live?" asked Kojo.

"I live up in the hills with my dad," Rafiki said.

"My dad makes drums and masks. He strings beads and shells. People like what he makes."

"What can we do to have fun?" asked Kojo.

"We can ride in my little boat," Rafiki said. "The ride will be lots of fun."

"Mama, can we go?" asked Ama.

"Yes, as long as Daddy and I can still see you," Mama said.

The three children got in the boat.

"Look down at the bottom of the boat," Rafiki said. "It's made of glass!"

"Hey, I can see all kinds of fish!" said Ama. "See the shells?" asked Rafiki.

"Look, I see a shark!" said Kojo.

"I don't see a shark!" said Ama. "I just see seaweed."

"Ha Ha, I was joking!" said Kojo. "There's no shark."

"Don't joke like that!" Rafiki said. "Sharks can hurt us. That was not funny."

"Where are we going?" Ama asked their new friend.

"We're going to the big cave right over there. We can play there."

The glass bottom boat floated near the big cave.

The children got out. Ama waved at Mama and Daddy. "Let's play hide and seek!" said Rafiki. "Ama can be 'It'."

"Count to ten," said Kojo. "Close your eyes. Don't peek!"

Ama began to count: "One, two, three, four, five, six, seven, eight, nine, ten. Ready or not, here I come!" she shouted.

Ama looked for Kojo. She did not see him. Ama looked for Rafiki. She did not see him. "Kojo! Rafiki! Where are you?" Ama laughed. "I can't find you!"

"Ama, we're over here by the big rock," Kojo yelled. "Come fast!"

"Look, Ama, look!" said Kojo. "Come see what we found in the cave!"

"It looks like a map," said Rafiki. "Maybe it will lead us to treasure!"

"I can't read a map," said Ama.

"It's not hard," said Rafiki. "The map can help us find the way to the treasure. Let's see what it says."

"First, the map says to run to the big rock," Rafiki said.

"Where is the big rock?" asked Ama.

"There it is," pointed Kojo.

Ama, Kojo and Rafiki ran to the big rock.

"What does the map tell us to do next?" Ama asked.

"It tells us to hop on one leg by the side of the cave."

Kojo, Ama and Rafiki hopped on one leg. "This is fun!" said Ama. They hopped by the side of the cave.

"Next, the map says to crawl on the sand to the palm tree. Then we are to walk five feet from the east side of the tree and dig in the sand."

Kojo and Ama crawled to the tree. Kojo walked five feet from one side of the tree. Ama walked five feet from the other side of the tree.

"Kojo, you're not on the east side of the tree!" said Ama. "The map said to go five feet and dig on the east side."

"There's no mark by the tree to tell which side is the east side," said Kojo. "I'll dig where I am," he said.

Kojo and Ama began to dig.

Rafiki sat down in the shade of the tree and smiled. "Look!" said Ama. "Look what I dug up," she said. "I dug up a drum, a doll, and a mask. I found the treasure!" she shouted with joy.

Kojo frowned. "I dug up a crab leg and a bug. I didn't find any treasure," he said. "This must not be the east side of the tree. I didn't know how to find the east."

"Did you know the treasure was in the sand?" Ama asked their new friend.

Rafiki winked and smiled at Kojo and Ama. "They are gifts for both of you," he said. "I made the map. That's what I do to have fun."

"You made a joke," said Ama, "but it was a good joke."

"That was a fun game," said Kojo, "but Ama, how did you know which side to dig on?"

Ama smiled. "I saw the sun when it came up," she said. "The sun always rises in the east. I just dug on the same side the sun came up on."

"That was smart!" said Kojo. "I'll know the east side next time. I don't want to miss out on more treasure!"

"I'll share the gifts with you," said Ama.

"Thank you," said Kojo. "You're a great sister!"

"Let's float back down the beach," Rafiki said. "Your mother and father are waving for us to come back."

KINGS AND QUEENS OF THE NILE

"Mama, Brother Shaka wants to take us to see the art show at the museum," said Ama. "Can we go?"

"Yes," said Mama, "but be back in time for lunch."

"What's the show about?" Kojo asked Brother Shaka. "It is about kings and queens of the Nile."

"What is the Nile?" asked Kojo.

"Who are the kings and queens?" asked Ama.

"The museum is not far," Brother Shaka said as he put on his red, black, and green cap. "We can talk as we walk."

Brother Shaka began his tale. "Once long, long ago there was a land in Africa. The name of the land was Kemet. People call it Egypt today. There is a river in the land called the Nile. It is the longest river in the world. The river made the land rich. The people had a good life."

"Tell us about the kings and queens!" said Ama.

"Many kings and queens of Kemet were very wise," said Brother Shaka. "They ruled their land well. They built pyramids to last for thousands and thousands of years. The Great Pyramid still stands strong today."

"What's a pyramid?" asked Kojo.

"A pyramid has a shape like a triangle but has four sides," Brother Shaka said. "The pyramids were built out of thousands of huge stones. The African people who built the pyramids were very, very wise."

"Tell us what the people of the Nile liked to do," said Kojo.

"Many people liked to paint pictures on the walls of the temples and tombs. The paintings tell us tales about the kings, queens and people of the land. They tell us about the great deeds the people did and how they showed their faith to the gods.

"There's the art museum!" said Kojo. "Let's go in."

"Look!" said Ama. "I see a cat. It's made of gold!"

"Sheba the Cat would have made many friends in long ago Kemet," said Brother Shaka. "The people of Kemet loved cats."

"Who is she?" asked Ama. "Was she a queen?"

"Hat-Shep-Sut was her name," said Brother Shaka. "She was a queen of Kemet. She was very beautiful and very wise."

"She looks like a strong queen," said Kojo.

"Yes, Hat-Shep-Sut was a strong queen," said Brother Shaka. "She took long trips to far off lands and did much to help her people. The people liked to paint tales about her on the walls. She was a great queen."

"Look at him!" said Kojo. "Was he a king?"

"Yes," said Brother Shaka. "His name was Tut-Ankh- Amun. His nickname was Tut."

"King Tut does not look very old," said Ama.

"Tut was just a boy when he was made king," Brother Shaka said. "He was only nine years old."

"Wow!" said Kojo. "A nine-year-old king! Can I be a king when I'm nine years old?" he asked.

"Can I be a queen when I'm nine years old?" asked Ama.

Brother Shaka touched his red, black, and green cap as he winked at Kojo and Ama. "If you are wise and do good deeds, you can be kings and queens right now," he said with a smile.

"Hey, look at King Tut's mask," said Ama. "It's made of gold!"

"King Tut was very rich," said Brother Shaka. "He had lots of gold."

"What did he like to do?" asked Kojo.

"King Tut liked to sail on the Nile in his boat. He liked to hunt with his spear. He liked to sit on the throne with his queen. King Tut and his queen liked to play a game. It was a stone game. They had lots of fun."

"How long did he rule as king?" asked Ama. "King Tut ruled for ten years," Brother Shaka said.

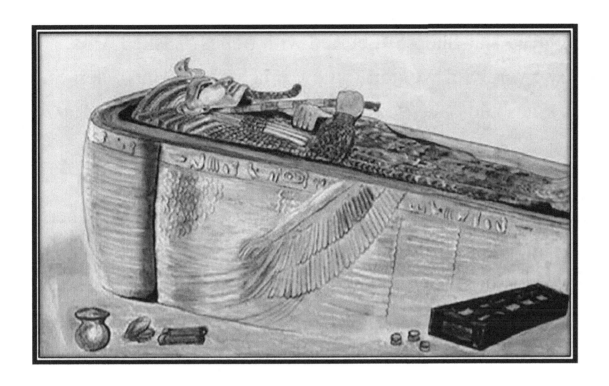

"When he died, he was put in a deep grave called a tomb. The gold mask was made to look like him. It was put on his face when he died. The people also put the stone game and lots of golden treasures inside his tomb."

"Why did they bury King Tut with all that treasure?" asked Ama.

"The people of Kemet felt that when they died, a part of them still lived on. They put oils and strips of cloth on the body so it would last a long time. They put things in the tombs that the kings and queens would need in their after- life. Many kings and queens of Kemet were buried with riches," Brother Shaka said.

"Was Queen Hat-Shep-Sut buried with riches?" asked Ama.

"Yes, she was. But we don't know much about Hat- Shep-Sut and the other kings and queens. We know the most about King Tut-Ankh-Amun."

"Why is that?" asked Kojo.

Brother Shaka took off his red, black, and green cap. "Robbers stole gold and treasure from most of the tombs thousands of years ago," he said with a frown. "The treasures would have helped to tell us more about the kings and queens. We know a lot about King Tut because his tomb was hidden for thousands of years. Since his tomb has been found, many of the golden treasures have been taken to museums in other lands for people to see."

"I like to look at the treasures here in the museum," said Kojo, "but I don't think Tut likes for them to be here. I think King Tut wants all of his gold and treasure to stay in his tomb near the Nile River!"

"I like the tales of long ago Kemet," said Ama. "They make me want to learn more about the African past."

SAVE THE LAND

Kojo and Ama rode with Mama on the train to see Great-grandpa. Great-grandpa lives in the south. He is very old. He can't see or hear well, but he is very wise.

Great-grandpa has a lot of land. The soil on his land is rich. The land has lots of trees on it. Great-grandpa planted many of these trees long ago.

"I'm going to shop at the big store in town," Mama said to Kojo and Ama. "I'll be back soon. Take care of your Great-grandpa."

"Great-grandpa, what's wrong?" asked Ama. "You are not smiling today."

"I'm not happy right now," said Great-grandpa.

"A man from the bank wants to take my land."

"Why does he want to take your land?" asked Kojo.

"He wants to cut down the trees on my land," said Great-grandpa.

"If you want to move, you can come to the city with us," said Ama.

"I don't want to move!" said Great-grandpa. "My roots are here. If my land could speak, it could tell the story of my life. I want to be buried on the land. Great-grandma is buried on the land. I want to stay close to her."

Just then, a man came to the porch. "Hey!" he yelled to Great-grandpa. "You must sell your land to me now!"

"I don't like the way he speaks to Great-grandpa," said Kojo.

"Put your name on the last line of this paper!" the man said to Great-grandpa.

"But I can't see well," Great-grandpa said. "I can't see what the paper says."

"It says the bank will give you a lot of cash," the man said. "Now put your name on the line!"

"Wait!" said Kojo. "I can see well. I'll read it to you."

Great-grandpa smiled. "Thank you, Kojo," he said.

"The paper says the bank will give you as much money as you paid for the land," said Kojo.

"That sounds like a good deal," said Ama.

"It may sound good," said Great-grandpa, "but it is a trick! I got the land a long, long time ago when it was real cheap. My land is worth at least ten times more money now! I will not put my name on the paper. I won't sell you my land."

The man from the bank left with a frown. "I'll be back!" he shouted.

"I am going inside to plan how to save my land," said Great-grandpa.

"We'll go play," said Kojo and Ama. "We're glad you didn't sell your land."

Just then two children came up to the porch. "Hi," said Ama. "Who are you?"

"My name is Nick," the boy said to Kojo and Ama.

"My name is Jane," said the girl. "That was our dad who just left," she said. "Can we play on the porch with you?"

"Sure," said Ama.

"Where do you live?" asked Kojo.

"We don't live near your great-grandpa," said Nick. "We live in town."

"What does your father do?" asked Ama.

"Our dad works at the bank," said Nick. "He likes lots of money. If your great-grandpa sells him his land, Dad can cut down the trees and make much more money!"

"What if Great-grandpa doesn't sell his land?" asked Ama.

"Friends of our dad will try to scare him off his land," said Nick.

"How will they try to scare him?" asked Ama.

Nick gave a big frown.

Jane gave a look of fear.

"They'll put white sheets over their heads," said Nick. "The sheets will have little holes cut in them for the eyes."

"Why will they wear sheets?" asked Kojo.

"They'll wear sheets so no one will see who they are," said Jane. "I heard them say they will burn a cross in his yard. Then your great-grandpa will have to leave."

"That's terrible!" said Ama.

"Jane and I don't like what they plan to do," said Nick. "But we don't know what to do to help your great-grandpa. We're just kids."

"You just helped us," said Ama. "Now we know the plan."

"We have to warn Great-grandpa!" Kojo said to Ama.

"It's time for us to go now," said Nick and Jane. "Bye."

"See you later," said Kojo. "Thanks for your help!"

"Mama went to town," said Ama. "Let's call Daddy on the phone. He'll know what to do."

"Hello Daddy," said Ama. "Great-grandpa is in trouble!" Ama told Daddy about the plan to scare Great-grandpa.

"Brother Shaka and I will come today," said Daddy. "It will take us four hours to get there."

"Who will feed Sheba the Cat?" asked Ama.

"We'll bring Sheba the Cat with us," said Daddy.

Daddy, Brother Shaka, and Sheba the Cat drove to Great-grandpa's land that day. It was a long ride.

"I'm glad you came to help!" Great-grandpa said. "I have a plan to stop these men."

Great-grandpa told Mama, Daddy, and Brother Shaka about his plan. It was a good plan. Daddy went to each farm. "Great-grandpa needs your help!" he said. "He does not want to leave his land. They must not force him to leave."

"We'll all help!" Great-grandpa's friends said. "We must work together to save the land."

"Kojo and Ama, go to the barn!" Mama said that night. "Take Sheba the Cat with you. The barn is far from the yard. You'll be safe there."

"But Mama," said Kojo and Ama, "we want to help. We're brave!"

"I know you're brave," Mama said. "But Daddy and I want to make sure you are safe."

Kojo, Ama, and Sheba the Cat ran to the barn. Great- grandpa's friends were on the front porch and the back porch. They were also in the yard and by the barn. They had no fear. They were strong.

"We will not be cheated out of our land anymore!" the people shouted.

Just then a pick-up truck full of men drove up.

"Peek out the hole on this side of the barn," said Kojo.

"I see the white sheets!" said Ama.

'Hiss, Hiss,' said Sheba the Cat.

"Look!" said Kojo. "I see Brother Shaka. The men with the white sheets don't see him. He has a strong rope. Look at him tie the rope from the back of the truck to the big tree!"

"I hope he doesn't let them see him," said Ama. "They won't like what he did."

Just then, Sheba the Cat ran out of the barn.

"Oh, no!" said Ama. "Sheba the Cat is gone."

Sheba ran and ran. She ran close to one of the men.

'Hiss, Hiss! This is a bad man!' she said. *'I will snag his sheet with my sharp claws.'*

Sheba the Cat made the man trip. The mask came off his face.

"Look!" one of Great-grandpa's friends shouted. "That man has a big store in town!"

"Oh, no!" the man cried. "They can see who I am. Let's get out of here!"

The men in the white sheets ran back to the truck. "We need to get out of here fast!" they said with fear.

The truck did not move. The rope held it fast to the tree.

"Oh, no!" the men said. "The truck won't budge! Let's run!!!"

Great-grandpa's friends ran after the men.

"Stop!" Daddy said. "Take off your sheets. Put your hands up!"

Sheba the Cat hissed. Mama took a camera out of her bag and took pictures.

"We'll make sure you don't do this again," Great- grandpa said.

"We will post your pictures all over the town," Mama said. "People will know who you are. They will frown when they see your pictures,"

"People won't want to put money in your bank. They won't want to shop at your store," Great-grandpa said.

"People won't trust you," Brother Shaka said. "We will show the pictures all over!" Daddy said. The men left in their truck. They were afraid.

Kojo and Ama ran from the barn. They hugged Great- grandpa. "We're glad they did not scare you off your land," said Kojo.

"Your Great-grandpa can not see or hear well," said Brother Shaka, "but he is very wise to keep his land!"

SHEBA THE CAT

A. Can You Answer These Questions?

    1. How did Ama let Kojo know she needed help?

    2. How did Sheba the Cat help Ama in this story?

    3. Where did Sheba the Cat find Kojo?

    4. How did Kojo help Ama in this story?

B. Which Sentences are True and Which are False?

    _____ Sheba the Cat is a bad pet.
    _____ Ama tied the note to Sheba's neck.
    _____ Ama tied the note to Sheba's tail.
    _____ Sheba the Cat brings good luck.
    _____ Sheba did not stop to chase the mouse.
    _____ Sheba stopped to play with Jack the Cat.
    _____ Kojo helped Ama.

C. How Did the Person Feel?

    1. Ama fell down and hurt her leg. She felt:
        a. happy
        b. sad

    2. Kojo read Ama's note. He felt:
        a. cheerful
        b. worried

    3. Kojo came to help Ama. Ama felt:
        a. glad
        b. mad

D. Activity

    Kojo and Ama are names from Ghana, West Africa. The following names from Ghana represent days of the week. Find out which day of the week you were born on and learn your Ghanaian name.

Day of Week	Boy	Girl	Meaning
Sunday	Kwesi	Akosua	Under the Sun
Monday	Kojo	Adjoa	Peace
Tuesday	Kwabena	Abena	Fire
Wednesday	Kwaku	Akua	Fame
Thursday	Yao	Yaa	Strength
Friday	Kofi	Afua	Growth
Saturday	Kwame	Ama	Most Ancient

NOTES FOR THE PARENT AND TEACHER

The Adventures of Kojo and Ama is a primer designed to strengthen and reinforce the reading skills of children who have been exposed to basic phonics. The primer reinforces short and long vowel sounds, consonant blends, digraphs, dipthongs and contractions. It also introduces new sight words. The stories are perfect for oral reading in the classroom. Students may take turns reading pages. Preschool children can begin to identify familiar words by sight as the parent/teacher reads the stories to them.

In addition to reinforcing phonic skills, *The Adventures of Kojo and Ama* explores values centering around responsibility, purpose, pride, self-esteem, unity and creativity. The book also exposes children to the importance of caution and safety, and helps to sensitize them to discrimination in society.

- **Purpose and Responsibility** are emphasized in the story "Sheba the Cat." Sheba did not allow anyone or anything to distract her from her purpose of getting help for Ama.

- **Pride and Self-Esteem** abound in both "The Man with the Red, Black, and Green Cap" and "Kings and Queens of the Nile." Brother Shaka acquaints Kojo and Ama with the genius of ancient Africa and some of the contributions to society made by African Americans. These chapters are designed for children, particularly those of African descent, to realize the richness of their heritage and culture.

- **Unity** is illustrated in the story "Save the Land" where the community comes together to help protect Great-grandpa.

- The necessity for **Safety and Caution** is portrayed through a valuable anti-drug message in the story "Danger in the Park After Dark." The story "Smoke and Flames" is embellished with important safety tips for the whole family.

- **Creativity** is demonstrated through Rafiki making the treasure map as the children have "Fun in the Sun."

- **Discrimination** is explored in the stories "The Man with the Red, Black, and Green Cap" and "Save the Land," where Kojo and Ama learn of injustices in their society.

Parents and teachers are encouraged to emphasize the above concepts and values with their children and students.

It is critical that children understand what they read, or what is read to them. Comprehension questions and activities corresponding to each story explore the child's understanding of the reading material. The parent or teacher can pose questions to the child to answer orally, or the questions can be reproduced on separate worksheets which provide adequate space for students to write their answers.

DANGER IN THE PARK AFTER DARK

A. Which Sentences Are True and Which Are False?

_____ The park is a good place to be when it's dark.

_____ Kojo tripped and fell down because his shoe was not tied.

_____ Kojo held the little bag because he liked the man with the stick.

_____ Kojo took the money from the stranger and bought some new shoes.

_____ Drugs can harm your body and mind.

B. Can You Pick the Right Answer?

    1. The main events in this story take place:

        a. at home

        b. at the zoo

        c. in the park

    2. The colors in Brother Shaka's cap are:

        a. red, white, blue

        b. yellow, green, black

        c. red, black, green

    3. The strangers ran away because:

        a. the police came

        b. Sheba scared them

        c. it was dark

C. Can You Answer These Questions?

    1. What do you think Kojo's big wish was for?

    2. How did Sheba the Cat help Kojo in this story?

    3. What lessons did Kojo learn in this story?

D. What Happened First?

    1. Kojo made a wish.

    2. Ama told Kojo about the big star.

    3. Kojo fell down because his shoe was not tied.

E. What Happened Last?

    1. Sheba the Cat jumped out of the tree.

    2. Daddy gave Kojo a big hug.

    3. Ama ran to get help.

THE MAN WITH THE RED, BLACK, AND GREEN CAP

A. Can You Pick the Right Answer?

    1. Who made the first clock in America?

        a. Benjamin Banneker

        b. Martin Luther King

        c. Harriet Tubman

    2. Who made the first stoplight?

        a. Rosa Parks

        b. Garrett Morgan

        c. Brother Shaka

    3. Daniel Hale Williams was:

        a. a doctor

        b. a lawyer

        c. a fire fighter

    4. Charles Drew is best known for his work with:

        a. blood

        b. libraries

        c. babies

    5. To check out a book from the library you need:

        a. money

        b. library card

        c. driver's license

    6. The red, black, and green colors in his cap made Brother Shaka feel:

        a. mad

        b. sad

        c. proud

B. Can You Answer These Questions?

    1. Why couldn't Brother Shaka's grandfather get blood from the hospital's blood bank?

    2. What did Brother Shaka say the colors red, black, and green in his cap stood for?

C. Which Sentences Are True and Which Are False?

    _____ Rosa Parks did not get out of her seat because she was lazy.

    _____ Rev. Martin Luther King helped to organize the bus boycott.

    _____ The bus boycott made the bus company rich.

SMOKE AND FLAMES

A. Can You Pick the Right Answer?
1. Where did Uncle Bob go to sleep?
   a. in bed
   b. on the chair
   c. on the porch
2. Why did Sheba try to wake Uncle Bob up?
   a. So he could watch TV and play cards.
   b. So he would not get hurt in the fire.
   c. So he would not snore so loud.

B. Can You Answer These Questions?
1. How did the fire start?
2. How did Sheba the Cat help Uncle Bob?

C. Which Sentences Are True and Which Are False?
_____ Mama and Daddy like everything Uncle Bob does.
_____ Smoking cigarettes is good for the lungs.
_____ The flame from the cigarette made the magazine burn.
_____ Uncle Bob woke up as soon as Sheba the Cat licked his face.
_____ Both the smoke and the flames from a fire can harm you.
_____ Smoke alarms must be checked to make sure they still work.

D. What Happened First?
1. The fire fighters put the fire out.
2. Kojo and Ama went to bed.
3. Sheba the Cat bit Uncle Bob's nose.

E. What Happened Last?
1. The family climbed down the ladder.
2. The magazine pages began to burn.
3. Mama stuffed rags to seal the crack in the door.

F. Activity
There should be at least one smoke alarm in every home. Ask your mother or father to show you where the smoke alarm(s) is(are) in your home. Remind them to check the batteries to make sure the alarm works. Draw a picture showing how you and your family would leave your home if there were a fire.

FUN IN THE SUN

A. Can You Pick the Right Answer?

    1. The main events in this story take place in:

        a. Africa

        b. Asia

        c. Jamaica

    2. What happened first in this story?

        a. Kojo dug up a crab leg and a bug.

        b. Kojo and Ama found the map.

        c. Kojo and Ama rode on the plane to Jamaica.

    3. What happened last in this story?

        a. Ama found the treasure.

        b. Kojo and Ama said goodbye to Brother Shaka.

        c. Kojo and Ama met their new friend, Rafiki.

B. Can You Answer These Questions?

    1. Why was Kojo's joke about the sharks a bad joke?

    2. Why was Rafiki's joke about the treasure a good joke?

    3. How did the treasure get in the sand?

C. Can You Make Up Your Own Story?

    While Kojo and Ama were in Jamaica, Sheba the Cat stayed in the big city with Brother Shaka. One day ...

D. Can You Give Directions?

    In the story Ama finds the treasure by following the directions on the map Rafiki made. Make up a map of your own giving directions leading to treasure.

E. Did You Know?

    Rafiki (Rah-FEE-kee) is a name from East Africa which means "friend". Here are some other names from Africa and their meanings. Use the internet or a book of African names to find a name that means something special to you.

Shaka	SHA-ka	a Zulu warrior king
Akili	Ah-KEE-lee	intelligent
Makini	Mah-KEE-nee	strength of character
Bomani	Boh-MAH-nee	warrior
Seitu	Say-EE-too	artist
Aisha	Ah-EE-sha	life
Tamia	Tah-MEE-ah	pace setter
Sekou	Say-KOO	fighter

KINGS AND QUEENS OF THE NILE

A. Can You Pick the Right Answer?

    1. A name for long ago Egypt was:
        a. Kemet
        b. Spain
        c. Nile

    2. How old was Tut-Ankh-Amun when he was made king?
        a. nineteen
        b. nine
        c. ninety

    3. What was King Tut's mask made from?
        a. gold
        b. paper
        c. silver

B. Can You Fill in the Blank?

    1. The Nile is the _____ river in the world.
        a. shortest
        b. longest
        c. newest

    2. Many kings and queens of Kemet were buried with _____.
        a. riches
        b. rags
        c. balloons

C. Can You Answer These Questions?

    1. Why does the story say Sheba the Cat would have made many friends in long ago Kemet?

    2. Why don't we know a lot about Queen Hat-Shep-Sut?

    3. Name two things King Tut liked to do.

    4. Name something that was put in King Tut's tomb when he died.

D. Activity

The people of Kemet liked to paint pictures on the walls of the temples and tombs. The paintings tell us tales about the kings, queens, and people of the land. Paint a picture which tells a story about something in your life.

SAVE THE LAND

A.   Can you pick the right answer?

    1. How did Kojo and Ama get to Great-grandpa's house?
- a.   by plane
- b.   by car
- c.   by train

    2. How long did it take Daddy and Brother Shaka to drive to Great-grandpa's land?
- a.   four hours
- b.   four minutes
- c.   four days

B.   Can you answer these questions?

    1.   Why didn't Great-grandpa want to sell his land?

    2.   Why did Great-grandpa say the man from the bank was trying to trick him?

    3.   How did Nick and Jane help Great-grandpa?

    4.   Why did Mama take pictures of the men?

C.   Which sentences are TRUE and which are FALSE?
_____ Great-grandpa was scared and sold his land.
_____ Great-grandpa's friends came to help him.
_____ Great-grandpa lives in the north.
_____ A cross was burned on Great-grandpa's land.
_____ Brother Shaka tied a rope from the back of the truck to a tree.
_____ Nick and Jane live in town.
_____ Sheba the Cat stayed in the big city with Brother Shaka.

D.   What happened First in this story?
1. Mama took pictures of the men.
2. Brother Shaka tied the rope to the tree.
3. Kojo read the paper to Great-grandpa.

E.   What happened Last?
1 Sheba the Cat made the man's mask come off.
2. Kojo and Arna rode on the train to Great-grandpa's house.
3. Great-grandpa's friends came to help him.

ABOUT THE AUTHOR

Nkechi Taifa is an attorney, activist, educator, author, and mother. She is the author of four books for young people: *The Adventures of Kojo and Ama, Shining Legacy, Three Tales of Wisdom*, and *Aisha and the Magic Ankh*. These books were originally written while teaching at an Independent Black School during the late 1970s and have now been republished for a new generation. She is also the author of the best-seller memoir – *Black Power, Black Lawyer: My Audacious Quest for Justice*, and a new rendition of *Reparations Yes*.

ABOUT THE ILLUSTRATOR

Afia Nson Bonsu is a multi-media artist, an educator since 1979, a writer and master seamstress. Founder of Rhythm-N-Flow Academy, she is a mother of four adult sons and daughters, and a grandmother. Other books she has illustrated include *Positive Images for African Children* and *You Spoke, Now I Listen*.

THE TAIFA TRILOGY OF TALES FOR A NEW GENERATION

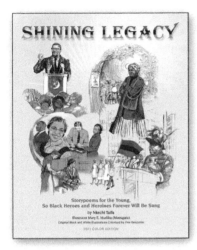

SHINING LEGACY:

Storypoems For The Young, So Black Heroes And Heroines Forever Will Be Sung

(Ages: 8 yrs old and up)

Shining Legacy celebrates the past through epic, ballad, legend and saga, all accentuated with rhyme. Role models range from Harriet Tubman, Rosa Parks, Fannie Lou Hamer, and Sojourner Truth – to Malcolm X, Denmark Vesey, Toussaint L'Ouverture, Paul Robeson, and Marcus Garvey.

THE ADVENTURES OF KOJO AND AMA

(Ages: 5 yrs old – 12 yrs old)

Journey with Kojo and Ama through seven adventures combining excitement, fun and suspense with lessons in pride and heritage. The children's heroic black cat Sheba brings them good luck as they find themselves in settings ranging from an inner city park to the deep South, and from the island of Jamaica to ancient Egypt.

THREE TALES OF WISDOM

(Ages: 8 yrs old and up)

Anansi's magic helps Ayanna get to the Harvest Festival, despite the fact that her two sisters fail to follow the Seven Principles of the value system …

A young brother growing up in New York City learns the story of the mighty Marcus Garvey …

Jabari finds wisdom through his encounters with spiders, lions, warriors, elephants, cockroaches, camels and birds …

Master Storyteller *Nkechi Taifa* resurrects and republishes her popular books for young people from over three decades ago as she brings her timeless wisdom for new generations to enjoy.

Made in the USA
Columbia, SC
13 October 2021